ALUN

The Sentry

The Corgi Series   *Writing from Wales*

The Corgi Series   Writing from Wales

Alun Lewis
The Sentry
Poems and stories

Series editor
Meic Stephens
Professor of Welsh Writing in English
University of Glamorgan

Carreg Gwalch Cyf.

ISBN: 0-86381-706-8

Cover design: Sian Parri

*First published in 2003 by
Carreg Gwalch Cyf., 12 Iard yr Orsaf, Llanrwst,
Wales LL26 0EH
☎ 01492 642031 🖷 01492 641502
✆ books@carreg-gwalch.co.uk
Internet: www.carreg-gwalch.co.uk*

*Supported by an 'Arts for All' Lottery grant
from the Arts Council of Wales*

*Carreg Gwalch Cyf. acknowledges the co-operation of
Gweno Lewis in the publication of these poems and stories.*

*The Editor is grateful for the advice of his colleague
Jeremy Hooker in the selection of these poems and stories.*

Contents

Alun Lewis (1915-44)

Alun Lewis was born on 1 July 1915 at Cwmaman, a mining village near Aberdare in Glamorgan; both his parents were schoolteachers. He was educated at Cowbridge Grammar School and went on to the University College of Wales, Aberystwyth, where he read History, and to Manchester University, where he took a master's degree. In 1938 he joined the staff of the Lewis Boys' School, Pengam, where he had a reputation as a gifted teacher, but resigned from the post in 1940 and, after much heart-searching and despite his pacifist convictions, joined the Army as a commissioned officer.

He found the officer's life distasteful and preferred the company of the men, most of whom came from the valleys of South Wales; but, under increasing stress, he resumed the writing of poems and stories which he had begun while at school. In July 1941 he married Gweno Ellis, whom he had met when they were undergraduates. In October of the year following his battalion of the South Wales Borderers was sent to India, where another period of intense literary activity began. The poverty and nihilism of India affected him deeply and he suffered again the bouts of depression that had dogged him for several years. In July 1943, in Karachi, he met and fell in love with a woman named Freda Aykroyd, and they had a brief affair.

In January 1944 he went with his regiment to Chittagong in Burma. There, as Intelligence Officer, he was given permission to move into a forward position facing the Japanese and, on 5 March, died of wounds received from his own revolver. He was buried in the war cemetery at Taukkyan.

Despite his comparatively small output, Alun Lewis was recognized as an accomplished writer during his own short lifetime. Serious, idealistic, devoted to those he loved, particularly his wife, and intent on serving humanity as a writer, he was concerned with what he called 'the twin themes of life and death', exploring them in verse and prose of a high order. 'My life belongs to the world. I will do what I can,' he makes a character say in 'They Came'. His two collections of poems were *Raiders' Dawn* (1942) and *Ha! Ha! Among the Trumpets* (1945); his stories were brought together in *The Last Inspection* (1943) and in the posthumous volume, *In the Green Tree* (1948). In everything he wrote there is compassion for the underdog, whether British soldier or Indian peasant, and a fine delight in the natural world, even in the parched landscapes of the sub-continent; but more than all, he saluted the integrity of good men and women, of whom we now know him to have been one. His was a tragic vision, forced to early maturity by his military experience, and his death the single greatest loss sustained by Welsh letters during the second world war.

Raiders' Dawn

Softly the civilized
Centuries fall,
Paper on paper,
Peter on Paul.

And lovers waking
From the night –
Eternity's masters,
Slaves of Time –
Recognize only
The drifting white
Fall of small faces
In pits of lime.

Blue necklace left
On a charred chair
Tells that Beauty
Was startled there.

All Day It Has Rained . . .

All day it has rained, and we on the edge of the
                                                moors
Have sprawled in our bell-tents, moody and dull
                                                as boors,
Groundsheets and blankets spread on the muddy
                                                ground
And from the first grey wakening we have found
No refuge from the skirmishing fine rain
And the wind that made the canvas heave and flap
And the taut wet guy-ropes ravel out and snap.
All day the rain has glided, wave and mist and
                                                dream,
Drenching the gorse and heather, a gossamer
                                                stream
Too light to stir the acorns that suddenly
Snatched from their cups by the wild south-
                                                westerly
Pattered against the tent and our upturned
                                                dreaming faces.
And we stretched out, unbuttoning our braces,
Smoking a Woodbine, darning dirty socks,
Reading the Sunday papers – I saw a fox
And mentioned it in the note I scribbled home; –
And we talked of girls, and dropping bombs on
                                                Rome,
And thought of the quiet dead and the loud
                                                celebrities

Exhorting us to slaughter, and the herded
                              refugees;
– Yet thought softly, morosely of them, and as
                              indifferently
As of ourselves or those whom we
For years have loved, and will again
To-morrow maybe love; but now it is the rain
Possesses us entirely, the twilight and the rain.

And I can remember nothing dearer or more to my
                              heart
Than the children I watched in the woods on
                              Saturday
Shaking down burning chestnuts for the
                    schoolyard's merry play,
Or the shaggy patient dog who followed me
By Sheet and Steep and up the wooded scree
To the Shoulder o'Mutton where Edward Thomas
                              brooded long
On death and beauty – till a bullet stopped his
                              song.

The Sentry

I have begun to die.
For now at last I know
That there is no escape
From Night. Not any dream
Nor breathless images of sleep
Touch my bat's-eyes. I hang
Leathery-arid from the hidden roof
Of Night, and sleeplessly
I watch within Sleep's province.
I have left
The lovely bodies of the boy and girl
Deep in each other's placid arms;
And I have left
The beautiful lanes of sleep
That barefoot lovers follow to this last
Cold shore of thought I guard.
I have begun to die
And the guns' implacable silence
Is my black interim, my youth and age,
In the flower of fury, the folded poppy,
Night.

To Edward Thomas

(On visiting the memorial stone above Steep in Hampshire)

I

On the way up from Sheet I met some children
Filling a pram with brushwood; higher still
Beside Steep church an old man pointed out
A rough white stone upon a flinty spur
Projecting from the high autumnal woods . . .
I doubt if much has changed since you came here
On your last leave; except the stone; it bears
Your name and trade: 'To Edward Thomas, Poet.'

II

Climbing the steep path through the copse I knew
My cares weighed heavily as yours, my gift
Much less, my hope
No more than yours.
And like you I felt sensitive and somehow apart,
Lonely and exalted by the friendship of the wind
And the placid afternoon enfolding
The dangerous future and the smile.

III

I sat and watched the dusky berried ridge
Of yew-trees, deepened by oblique dark shafts,
Throw back the flame of red and gold and russet

That leapt from beech and ash to birch and
                                    chestnut
Along the downward arc of the hill's shoulder,
And sunlight with discerning fingers
Softly explore the distant wooded acres,
Touching the farmsteads one by one with lightness
Until it reached the Downs, whose soft green
                                    pastures
Went slanting sea- and skywards to the limits
Where sight surrenders and the mind alone
Can find the sheeps' tracks and the grazing.

And for that moment Life appeared
As gentle as the view I gazed upon.

IV

Later, a whole day later, I remembered
This war and yours and your weary
Circle of failure and your striving
To make articulate the groping voices
Of snow and rain and dripping branches
And love that ailing in itself cried out
About the straggling eaves and ringed the candle
With shadows slouching round your buried head;
And in the lonely house there was no ease
For you, or Helen, or those small perplexed
Children of yours who only wished to please.
Divining this, I knew the voice that called you
Was soft and neutral as the sky

Breathing on the grey horizon, stronger
Than night's immediate grasp, the limbs of mercy
Oblivious as the blood; and growing clearer,
More urgent as all else dissolved away,
– Projected books, half-thoughts, the children's
                                        birthdays,
And wedding anniversaries as cold
As dates in history – the dream
Emerging from the fact that folds a dream,
The endless rides of stormy-branchèd dark
Whose fibres are a thread within the hand –

Till suddenly, at Arras, you possessed that hinted
                                        land.

Post-Script: for Gweno

If I should go away,
Beloved, do not say
'He has forgotten me'.
For you abide,
A singing rib within my dreaming side;
You always stay.
And in the mad tormented valley
Where blood and hunger rally
And Death the wild beast is uncaught, untamed,
Our soul withstands the terror
And has its quiet honour
Among the glittering stars your voices named.

From 'War Wedding'

The Marriage Bed

Draw a green cedar over the peeping sky,
Latch the grey sash across the glancing sea,
Close the dark door and lie within the rose,
Beloved, lie with me.

My heavy boots stand sentinel against
This hired bedroom underneath the eaves,
Where Beauty slips the green leash of her Spring
And flowers blossom from a ring of leaves.

And in her white magnetic fields
My tense prismatic fingers move
In patterns of attraction and release;
The parallels tend unswervingly
Towards the pole of peace.

The fragile universe of self
In all its fine integrity
Becomes a cosmic curve, a thrust
Of natural fertility;
And Gods who shivered in the dust
Have found their lost divinity.

And if to-night it chance we weep,
None shall know of our distress;
We are the bread and wine who share the feast;
The elements are in our nakedness.

Black cedar, hide the peeping day;
Sun, lie awhile beneath the sea;
And rose, within your velvet heart
Keep her, and me.

The Mountain over Aberdare

From this high quarried ledge I see
The place for which the Quakers once
Collected clothes, my fathers' home,
Our stubborn bankrupt village sprawled
In jaded dusk beneath its nameless hills;
The drab streets strung across the cwm,
Derelict workings, tips of slag
The gospellers and gamblers use
And children scrutting for the coal
That winter dole cannot purvey;
Allotments where the collier digs
While engines hack the coal within his brain;
Grey Hebron in a rigid cramp,
White cheap-jack cinema, the church
Stretched like a sow beside the stream;
And mourners in their Sunday best
Holding a tiny funeral, singing hymns
That drift insidious as the rain
Which rises from the steaming fields
And swathes about the skyline crags
Till all the upland gorse is drenched
And all the creaking mountain gates
Drip brittle tears of crystal peace;
And in a curtained parlour women hug
Huge grief, and anger against God.

But now the dusk, more charitable than Quakers,
Veils the cracked cottages with drifting may
And rubs the hard day off the slate.
The colliers squatting on the ashtip
Listen to one who holds them still with tales,
While that white frock that floats down the dark
                                        alley
Looks just like Christ; and in the lane
The clink of coins among the gamblers
Suggests the thirty pieces of silver.
I watch the clouded years
Rune the rough foreheads of these moody hills,
This wet evening, in a lost age.

Dawn on the East Coast

From Orford Ness to Shingle Street
The grey disturbance spreads
Washing the icy seas on Deben Head.

Cock pheasants scratch the frozen fields,
Gulls lift thin horny legs and step
Fastidiously among the rusted mines.

The soldier leaning on the sandbagged wall
Hears in the combers' curling rush and crash
His single self-centred monotonous wish;

And time is a froth of such transparency
His drowning eyes see what they wish to see;
A girl laying his table with a white cloth.

* * *

The light assails him from a flank,
Two carbons touching in his brain
Crumple the cellophane lanterns of his dream.

And then the day, grown feminine and kind,
Stoops with the gulfing motion of the tide
And pours his ashes in a tiny urn.
From Orford Ness to Shingle Street
The grey disturbance lifts its head
And one by one, reluctantly,
The living come back slowly from the dead.

Goodbye

So we must say Goodbye, my darling,
And go, as lovers go, for ever;
Tonight remains, to pack and fix on labels
And make an end of lying down together.

I put a final shilling in the gas,
And watch you slip your dress below your knees
And lie so still I hear your rustling comb
Modulate the autumn in the trees.

And all the countless things I shall remember
Lay mummy-cloths of silence round my head;
I fill the carafe with a drink of water;
You say 'We paid a guinea for this bed,'

And then, 'We'll leave some gas, a little warmth
For the next resident, and these dry flowers,'
And turn your face away, afraid to speak
The big word, that Eternity is ours.

Your kisses close my eyes and yet you stare
As though God struck a child with nameless fears;
Perhaps the water glitters and discloses
Time's chalice and its limpid useless tears.

Everything we renounce except our selves;
Selfishness is the last of all to go;
Our sighs are exhalations of the earth,
Our footprints leave a track across the snow.

We made the universe to be our home,
Our nostrils took the wind to be our breath,
Our hearts are massive towers of delight,
We stride across the seven seas of death.

Yet when all's done you'll keep the emerald
I placed upon your finger in the street;
And I will keep the patches that you sewed
On my old battledress tonight, my sweet.

The Departure

Eyes closed, half waking, that first morning
He felt the curved grey bows enclose him,
The voyage beginning, the oceans giving way
To the thrust of steel, the pulse and beat
Of the engines that even now were revolving,
Revolving, rotating, throbbing along his brain
Rattling the hurried carpentry of his bunk,
Setting an unknown bearing into space.

He never thought that he might doubt or fear
Or lose himself or kill an honest man
Or die in some street outrage. Always there
Beneath the exertion and the novelty
Would be the deep sad rhythm of the process
Of the created thing awaking to the sound of the
                                    engine.

And he remembered all that was prevented,
How she came with him to the barrier
And knowing she could come no further
Turned back on the edge of his sleep,
Vexed, fumbling in her handbag,
Giving the world a dab of rouge and powder,
A toss of head, a passing hatred,
Going in all these trivial things, yet proudly;
Knowing more deeply than he the threat of his
                                    voyage,
With all a living woman's fear of death.

He heard the seagulls crying round the porthole
And in his sleepy trouble he knew the chafing
Of nettles her hands would be weaving into a
                              garment
To turn her white-winged lover back to man,
A man released from the weary fluctuations
Of time and distance, forgetfulness and dying.

And then he woke unrested from his longing,
And locked himself and hurried to off-load
Boxes of ammunition from the wagons
And send them swaying from the groaning
                              derricks
Deep into the unrefusing ship.

On Embarkation

I

Consider this silent disciplined assembly
Close squadded in the dockyard's hooded lamps,
Each blur a man with some obscure trouble
Or hard regret as bulky as the cargo
The cranking derricks drop into the hold.
Think of them, as the derrick sways and poises
Vacantly as their minds do at this passage,
Good-natured agents of a groping purpose
That sends them now to strange precipitous places
Where all are human and Oh easily hurt
And – the temptation being to forget
Such villages as linger in the mind,
Lidice on the road from Bethlehem –
Ask whether kindness will persist in hearts
Plagued by the snags and rapids of a curse,
And whether the fortunate few will still attain
The sudden flexible grasp of a dangerous problem
And feel their failures broaden into manhood,
Or take the Bren's straightforward road
And grow voluptuous at the sight of blood?
Each of us is invisible to himself,
Our eyes grow neutral in the long Unseen,
We take or do not take a hand of cards,
We shake down nightly in the strange Unknown.
Yet each one has a hankering in the blood,

A dark relation that disturbs his joke
And will not be abandoned with a shrug:
Each has a shrunken inkling of the Good.
And one man, wrapped in blankets, solemnly
Remembers as he bites his trembling nails
The white delightful limbs, the nest of peace.
And one who misses what it's all about,
Sick with injections, sees the 'tween-decks turn
To fields of home, each tree with its rustling
                              shadow
Slipped like a young girl's dress down to its ankles;
Where lovers lay in chestnut shadows,
And horses came there from the burning meadows.
And these things stay, in seasonal rotation
Within the cycles of our false intention.

But others, lacking the power of reflection,
Broke ship, impelled by different emotions.
The police are seeking men of their description
As sedulously as their own promotion.

II

Before he sails a man may go on leave
To any place he likes, where he's unknown
Or where he's mentioned with a warm inflection
And hands are shaken up and down the street.
Some men avoid this act of recognition
And make the world a dartboard for their fling;
Oblivion is the colour of brown ale;

Peace is the backseat in the cinema.
But most men seek the place where they were born.

For me it was a long slow day by train.

Just here you leave this Cardiganshire lane,
Here by these milk churns and this telegraph pole,
Latch up the gate and cut across the fields.
Some things you see in detail, those you need;
The raindrops spurting from the trodden stubble
Squirting your face across the reaping meadow,
The strange machine-shaped scarab beetle
His scalloped legs clung bandy to a stalk,
The Jew's-harp bee with saddlebags of gold,
The wheat as thin as hair on flinty slopes,
The harsh hewn faces of the farming folks,
Opinion humming like a nest of wasps,
The dark-clothed brethren at the chapel gates;
And farther on the mortgaged crumbling farm
Where Shonni Rhys, that rough backsliding man
Has found the sheep again within the corn
And fills the evening with his sour oaths;
The curse of failure's in his shambling gait.
At last the long wet sands, the shelving beach,
The green Atlantic, far as eye can reach.
And what is here but what was always here
These twenty years, elusive as a dream
Flowing between the grinding-stones of fact –
A girl's affections or a new job lost,

A lie that burns the soft stuff in the brain,
Lust unconfessed, a scholarship let go
Or gained too easily, without much point –
Each hurt a search for those old country gods
A man takes with him in his native tongue
Finding a friendly word for all things strange,
The firm authentic truth of roof and rain.
And on the cliff's green brink where nothing stirs,
Unless the wind should stir it, I perceive
A child grow shapely in the loins I love.

III

In all the ways of going who can tell
The real from the unjustified farewell?
Women have sobbed when children left for school
Or husbands took the boat train to pursue
Contracts more tenuous than the marriage vow.
But now each railway station makes and breaks
The certain hold and drifts us all apart.
Some women know exactly what's implied.
Ten Years, they say behind their smiling eyes,
Thinking of children, pensions, looks that fade,
The slow forgetfulness that strips the mind
Of its apparel and wears down the thread;
Or maybe when he laughs and bends to make
Her laugh with him she sees that he must die
Because his eyes declare it plain as day.
And it is here, if anywhere, that words
– Debased like money by the same diseases –

Cast off the habitual clichés of fatigue
– The women hoping it will soon blow over,
The fat men saying it depends on Russia –
And all are poets when they say Goodbye
And what they say will live and fructify.

IV

And so we wait the tide, and when the dark
Laps round the swelling entrance to the sea
The grey evasive ship slips into line.
The bell clangs in the engine room, the night
Shrouds the cold faces watching at the rail.
Till suddenly from headland and from wharves
The searchlights throw their lambent bluish cloaks
Clothing the fairway in a sheen of silk.
The steel bows break, the churning screw burns
                                        white.
Each pallid face wears an unconscious smile.
And I – I pray my unborn tiny child
Has five good senses and an earth as kind
As the sweet breast of her who gives him milk
And waves me down this first clandestine mile.

Song

(On seeing dead bodies floating off the Cape)

The first month of his absence
I was numb and sick
And where he'd left his promise
Life did not turn or kick.
The seed, the seed of love was sick.

The second month my eyes were sunk
In the darkness of despair,
And my bed was like a grave
And his ghost was lying there.
And my heart was sick with care.

The third month of his going
I thought I heard him say
'Our course deflected slightly
On the thirty-second day –'
The tempest blew his words away.

And he was lost among the waves,
His ship rolled helpless in the sea,
The fourth month of his voyage
He shouted grievously
'Beloved, do not think of me.'

The flying fish like kingfishers
Skim the sea's bewildered crests,
The whales blow steaming fountains,
The seagulls have no nests
Where my lover sways and rests.

We never thought to buy and sell
This life that blooms or withers in the leaf,
And I'll not stir, so he sleeps well,
Though cell by cell the coral reef
Builds an eternity of grief.

But oh! the drag and dullness of my Self;
The turning seasons wither in my head;
All this slowness, all this hardness,
The nearness that is waiting in my bed,
The gradual self-effacement of the dead.

To Rilke

Rilke, if you had known that I was trying
To speak to you perhaps you would have said
'Humanity has her darlings to whom she's
                                    entrusted
A farthing maybe, or a jewel, at least a perception
Of what can develop and what must be always
                                    endured
And what the live may answer to the dead.
Such ones are known by their faces,
At least their absence is noted;
And they never lack an occasion,
They, the devoted.'

But I have to seek the occasion.
Labour, fatigue supervene;
The glitter of sea and land, the self-assertion
These fierce competing times insist upon.

Yet sometimes, seeking, hours glided inwards,
Laying their soft antennae on my heart,
And I forgot the thousand leagues I'd journeyed
As if Creation were about to start.

I watched the pure horizon for the earth
To rise in grey bare peaks that might enfold
The empty crumbling soil between the hands
Or coloured things a child's small fist might hold

Delightedly; I knew that unknown lands
Were near and real, like an act of birth.

Then I fell ill and restless.
Sweating and febrile all one burning week,
I hungered for the silence you acquired
And *envied* you, as though it were a gift
Presented on a birthday to the lucky.
For that which IS I thought you need not seek.

The sea is gone now and the crowded tramp
Sails other seas with other passengers.
I sit within the tent, within the darkness
Of India, and the wind disturbs my lamp.

The jackals howl and whimper in the nullah,
The goatherd sleeps upon a straw-piled bed,
And I know that in this it does not matter
Where one may be or what fate lies ahead.

And Vishnu, carved by some rude pious hand,
Lies by a heap of stones, demanding nothing
But the simplicity that she and I
Discovered in a way you'd understand
Once and for ever, Rilke, but in Oh a distant land.

The Mahratta Ghats

The valleys crack and burn, the exhausted plains
Sink their black teeth into the horny veins
Straggling the hills' red thighs, the bleating goats –
– Dry bents and bitter thistles in their throats –
Thread the loose rocks by immemorial tracks.
Dark peasants drag the sun upon their backs.

High on the ghat the new turned soil is red,
The sun has ground it to the finest red,
It lies like gold within each horny hand.
Siva has spilt his seed upon this land.

Will she who burns and withers on the plain
Leave, ere too late, her scraggy herds of pain,
The cow-dung fire and the trembling beasts,
The little wicked gods, the grinning priests,
And climb, before a thousand years have fled,
High as the eagle to her mountain bed
Whose soil is fine as flour and blood-red?

But no! She cannot move. Each arid patch
Owns the lean folk who plough and scythe and
                                        thatch
Its grudging yield and scratch its stubborn stones.
The small gods suck the marrow from their bones.

Who is it climbs the summit of the road?
Only the beggar bumming his dark load.
Who was it cried to see the falling star?
Only the landless soldier lost in war.

And did a thousand years go by in vain?
And does another thousand start again?

Water Music

Deep in the heart of the lake
Where the last light is clinging
A strange foreboding voice
Is patiently singing.

Do not fear to venture
Where the last light trembles
Because you were in love.
Love never dissembles.

Fear no more the boast, the bully,
The lies, the vain labour.
Make no show for death
As for a rich neighbour.

What stays of the great religions?
An old priest, an old birth.
What stays of the great battles?
Dust on the earth.

Cold is the lake water
And dark as history.
Hurry not and fear not
This oldest mystery.

This strange voice singing,
This slow deep drag of the lake,
This yearning, yearning, this ending
Of the heart and its ache.

In Hospital: Poona (I)

Last night I did not fight for sleep
But lay awake from midnight while the world
Turned its slow features to the moving deep
Of darkness, till I knew that you were furled,

Beloved, in the same dark watch as I.
And sixty degrees of longitude beside
Vanished as though a swan in ecstasy
Had spanned the distance from your sleeping side.

And like to swan or moon the whole of Wales
Glided within the parish of my care:
I saw the green tide leap on Cardigan,
Your red yacht riding like a legend there,

And the great mountains, Dafydd and Llewelyn,
Plynlimmon, Cader Idris and Eryri
Threshing the darkness back from head and fin,
And also the small nameless mining valley

Whose slopes are scratched with streets and
                                    sprawling graves
Dark in the lap of firwoods and great boulders
Where you lay waiting, listening to the waves –
My hot hands touched your white despondent
                                    shoulders

– And then ten thousand miles of daylight grew
Between us, and I heard the wild daws crake
In India's starving throat; whereat I knew
That Time upon the heart can break
But love survives the venom of the snake.

The Peasants

The dwarf barefooted, chanting
Behind the oxen by the lake,
Stepping lightly and lazily among the thorntrees
Dusky and dazed with sunlight, half awake;

The women breaking stones upon the highway,
Walking erect with burdens on their heads,
One body growing in another body,
Creation touching verminous straw beds.

Across scorched hills and trampled crops
The soldiers straggle by.
History staggers in their wake.
The peasants watch them die.

Burma Casualty

(To Capt. G.T. Morris, Indian Army)

I

Three endless weeks of sniping all the way,
Lying up when their signals rang too close,
– 'Ooeee, Ooee,' like owls, the lynx-eyed Jap, –
Sleeplessly watching, knifing, falling back.
And now the Sittang river was there at last
And the shambles of trucks and corpses round
                                        the bridge
And the bridge was blown. And he laughed.

And then a cough of bullets, a dusty cough
Filleted all his thigh from knee to groin.
The kick of it sucked his face into the wound.
He crumpled, thinking 'Death'. But no, not yet.
The femoral artery wasn't touched.
Great velour cloaks of darkness floated up.
But he refused, refused the encircling dark,
A lump of bitter gristle that refused.
The day grew bloodshot as they picked him up.

II

Lying in hospital he often thought
Of that darkness, whence it came
And how it played the enchantress in a grain
Of morphia or a nodding of the head

40

Late in the night and offered to release
The Beast that breathed with pain and ran with pus
Among the jumping fibres of the flesh.
And then he saw the Padre by his cot
With the Last Unction: and he started up.

III

'Your leg must go. Okay?' the surgeon said
'Take it' he said. 'I hate the bloody thing.'
Yet he was terrified – not of the knives
Nor losing that green leg (he'd often wished
He'd had a gun to shoot the damned thing off)
But of the darkness that he knew would come
And bid him enter its deep gates alone.

The nurse would help him and the orderlies.
But did they know? And could a rubber tube
Suck all that darkness out of lungs and heart?
'Open and close your fist – slowly,' the doctor said.
He did so, lying still upon his back.
The whitewashed walls, the windows bright with
sky
Gathered a brilliant light above his head.
Here was the light, the promise hard and pure,
His wife's sweet body and her wilful eyes.
Her timeless love stooped down to raise him up.
He felt the white walls part – the needle pricked,
'Ten seconds and you'll fade,' the doctor said.
He lay and looked into the snowwhite skies

For all ten seconds means at such a time.
Then through the warped interstices of life
The darkness swept like water through a boat
In gouts and waves of softness, claiming him . . .

He went alone: knew nothing: and returned
Retching and blind with pain, and yet Alive.

IV

Mending, with books and papers and a fan
Sunlight on parquet floors and bowls of flame
He heard quite casually that his friends were dead,
His regiment too butchered to reform.
And he lay in the lightness of the ward
Thinking of all the lads the dark enfolds
So secretly.
         And yet a man may walk
Into and through it, and return alive.
Why had his friends all stayed there, then?
He knew.
The dark is a beautiful singing sexless angel
Her hands so soft you scarcely feel her touch
Gentle, eternally gentle, round your heart.
She flatters and unsexes every man.

And Life is only a crude, pigheaded churl
Frowsy and starving, daring to suffer alone.

Bivouac

There was no trace of Heaven
That night as we lay
Punch-drunk and blistered with sunlight
On the ploughed-up clay.

I remembered the cactus where our wheels
Had bruised it, bleeding white;
And a fat rat crouching beadyeyed
Caught by my light;

And the dry disturbing whispers
Of the agitated wood,
With its leathery vendetta,
Mantillas dark with blood.

And the darkness drenched with Evil
Haunting as a country song,
Ignoring the protesting cry
Of Right and of Wrong.

Yet the peasant was drawing water
With the first excited bird
And the dawn with childish eyes
Observed us as we stirred.

And the milk-white oxen waited
Docile at the yoke
As we clipped on our equipment
And scarcely spoke.

Being bewildered by the night
And only aware
Of the withering obsession
That lovers grow to fear
When the last note is written
And at last and alone
One of them wakes in terror
And the other is gone.

The Jungle

I

In mole-blue indolence the sun
Plays idly on the stagnant pool
In whose grey bed black swollen leaf
Holds Autumn rotting like an unfrocked priest.
The crocodile slides from the ochre sand
And drives the great translucent fish
Under the boughs across the running gravel.
Windfalls of brittle mast crunch as we come
To quench more than our thirst – our selves –
Beneath this bamboo bridge, this mantled pool
Where sleep exudes a sinister content
As though all strength of mind and limb must pass
And all fidelities and doubts dissolve,
The weighted world a bubble in each head,
The warm pacts of the flesh betrayed
By the nonchalance of a laugh,
The green indifference of this sleep.

II

Wandering and fortuitous the paths
We followed to this rendezvous today
Out of the mines and offices and dives,
The sidestreets of anxiety and want,
Huge cities known and distant as the stars,
Wheeling beyond our destiny and hope.

We did not notice how the accent changed
As shadows ride from precipice to plain
Closing the parks and cordoning the roads,
Clouding the humming cultures of the West –
The weekly bribe we paid the man in black,
The day shift sinking from the sun,
The blinding arc of rivets blown through steel,
The patient queues, headlines and slogans flung
Across a frightened continent, the town
Sullen and out of work, the little home
Semi-detached, suburban, transient
As fever or the anger of the old,
The best ones on some specious pretext gone.

But we who dream beside this jungle pool
Prefer the instinctive rightness of the poised
Pied kingfisher deep darting for a fish
To all the banal rectitude of states,
The dew-bright diamonds on a viper's back
To the slow poison of a meaning lost
And the vituperations of the just.

III

The banyan's branching clerestories close
The noon's harsh splendour to a head of light.
The black spot in the focus grows and grows:
The vagueness of the child, the lover's deep
And inarticulate bewilderment,
The willingness to please that made a wound,

The kneeling darkness and the hungry prayer;
Cargoes of anguish in the holds of joy,
The smooth deceitful stranger in the heart,
The tangled wrack of motives drifting down
An oceanic tide of Wrong.
And though the state has enemies we know
The greater enmity within ourselves.

Some things we cleaned like knives in earth,
Kept from the dew and rust of Time
Instinctive truths and elemental love,
Knowing the force that brings the teal and quail
From Turkestan across the Himalayan snows
To Kashmir and the South alone can guide
That winging wildness home again.

Oh you who want us for ourselves,
Whose love can start the snow-rush in the woods
And melt the glacier in the dark coulisse,
Forgive this strange inconstancy of soul,
The face distorted in a jungle pool
That drowns its image in a mort of leaves.

IV

Grey monkeys gibber, ignorant and wise.
We are the ghosts, and they the denizens;
We are like them anonymous, unknown,
Avoiding what is human, near,
Skirting the villages, the paddy fields

Where boys sit timelessly to scare the crows
On bamboo platforms raised above their lives.

A trackless wilderness divides
Joy from its cause, the motive from the act:
The killing arm uncurls, strokes the soft moss;
The distant world is an obituary,
We do not hear the tappings of its dread.
The act sustains; there is no consequence.
Only aloneness, swinging slowly
Down the cold orbit of an older world
Than any they predicted in the schools,
Stirs the cold forest with a starry wind,
And sudden as the flashing of a sword
The dream exalts the bowed and golden head
And time is swept with a great turbulence,
The old temptation to remould the world.

The bamboos creak like an uneasy house;
The night is shrill with crickets, cold with space.
And if the mute pads on the sand should lift
Annihilating paws and strike us down
Then would some unimportant death resound
With the imprisoned music of the soul?
And we become the world we could not change?
Or does the will's long struggle end
With the last kindness of a foe or friend?

Midnight in India

Here is no mined and cratered deep
As in the fenced-off landscapes of the West
Within this Eastern wilderness
The human war is lost.

The three dark quarters bow their heads
To where the fourth in radiance glows;
The withered villages look up and smile;
The moon's annunciation grows.

Oh I have set the earth aflame
And brought the high dominions down,
And soiled each simple act with shame
And had no feelings of my own.

I sank in drumming tides of grief
And in the sea-king's sandy bed
Submerged in gulfs of disbelief
Lay with the redtoothed daughters of the dead.

Until you woke me with a sigh
And eased the dark compression in my head
And sang and did not cease when I
Broke your heart like holy bread.

We cast away the bitter death
That holds the fine circumference of life
And gathered in a single breath
All that begins and ends in man and wife

And though the painful errors grow
And youth sprawls dead beside the Gate
And lovely bodies stiffen in the snow
And old devotions breed a newer hate,

Yet time stands still upon the east
The moonlight lies in pools and human pain
Soothes the dry lips on which it lies
And I behold your calm white face again.

Mysterious tremors stir the beast,
In unknown worlds he dies;
I lie within your hands, within your peace,
And watch this last effulgent world arise.

They Came

The evening was slowly curdling the sky as the soldier trudged the last mile along the lane leading from the station to the Hampshire village where he was billeted. The hedgerows drew together in the dusk and the distance, bending their waving heads to each other as the fawn bird and the black bird sang among the green hollies. The village lay merged in the soft seaward slope of the South Downs; the soldier shifted his rifle from left to right shoulder and rubbed his matted eyelashes with his knuckles. He was a young chap but, hampered by his heavy greatcoat and equipment, he dragged his legs like an old clerk going home late. He cleared his throat of all that the train journey, cigarettes and chocolate and tea and waiting, had secreted in his mouth. He spat the thick saliva out. It hung on a twig.

Someone was following him. When he heard the footsteps first he had hurried, annoyed by the interfering sound. But his kit was too clumsy to hurry in and he was too tired. So he dawdled, giving his pursuer a chance to pass him. But the footsteps stayed behind, keeping a mocking interval. He couldn't stop himself listening to them, but he refused to look back. He became slowly angry with himself for letting them occupy his mind and possess his attention. After a while they seemed to come trotting out of the past in him, out of the Welsh mining village, the colliers gambling in the quarry, the county school where he learned of sex and of knowledge, and college where he had swotted and slacked in poverty, and boozed, and quarrelled in love. They were the footsteps of the heavy-jawed deacon of Zion, with his white grocer's apron and his hairy nostrils sniffing out corruption.

But that was silly, he knew. Too tired to control his mind, that's what it was. These footsteps were natural and English, the postman's perhaps . . . But still they followed him, and the dark gods wrestling in him in the mining valley pricked their goaty ears at the sound of the pimping feet.

He turned the corner into the village and went down the narrow street past the post office and the smithy, turned the corner under the A.A. sign and crossed the cobbled yard of the hotel where the officers' and business men's cars were parked. A shaggy old dog came frisking out of its straw-filled barrel in the corner, jumping and barking. He spoke to it and at once it grovelled on its belly. He always played with the dog in the mornings, between parades. The unit did its squad drill in the hotel yard, kitchen maids watching flirtatiously through the windows, giggling, and the lavatory smelling either of disinfectant or urine.

He pushed open the little door in the big sliding

doors of the garage which had been converted into a barrack room for the duration. Thin electric bulbs high in the cold roof dangled a weak light from the end of the twisted, wavering flex. Grey blankets folded over biscuits or straw palliasses down both sides of the room. Equipment hanging from nails on the whitewashed wall – in one corner a crucifix, over the thin, chaste, taciturn Irish boy's bed. He was the only one in the room, sitting on his bed in the cold dark corner writing in his diary. He looked up and smiled politely, self-effacingly, said 'Hallo. Had a good leave?' and bent his narrow head again to read what he'd written.

'Yes, thanks,' said the soldier, 'except for raids. The first night I was home he raided us for three hours, the sod,' he said, unbuckling his bayonet belt and slipping his whole kit off his shoulders.

Last time he returned from leave, four months back, he had sat down on his bed and written to his wife. They had married on the first day of that leave and slept together for six nights. This time he didn't ferret in his kitbag for notepaper and pencil. He went straight out.

The hotel management had set a room aside for the soldiers to booze in. It was a good class hotel, richly and vulgarly furnished with plush and mirrors and dwarf palms in green boxes. The auctioneers and lawyers and city men, the fishermen and golfers and bank managers, most of whom had week-end cottages or villas of retirement in commanding positions at the local beauty spots, spent the evening in the saloon bar and lounge, soaking and joking. So the soldiers were given a bare little bar parlour at the back, with a fire and a dartboard and two sawdust spitoons. The soldiers were glad of it. It was their own. They invited some of their pals from the village to play darts with them – the cobbler, the old dad who lived by himself in the church cottage and never shaved or washed, the poacher who brought them a plucked pheasant under his old coat sometimes – all the ones the soldiers liked popped in for an evening. A few girls, too, before the dance in the church hall, on Tuesdays.

Fred Garstang, from Portsmouth, and Ben Bryant, from Coventry, the two eldest soldiers in the unit – regulars who had never earned a stripe – were playing darts, two empty pint glasses on the mantelpiece by the chalk and duster.

''Owdee, Taffy?' they said in unison. ''Ave a good leave, lad?'

'Yes thanks,' he said automatically, 'except for raids. The sod raided us for three hours the first night I was home.'

'Damn. Just the wrong side of it,' said Fred, examining the quivering dart. 'I deserve to lose this bloody game, Ben. I 'xpect you're same as me, Taff; glad to get back to a bit of peace and quiet and a good sleep. My seven days in Pompey's the worst I've ever spent in India, China, the Rhineland, Gallygurchy or anywhere. But we're nice and cosy here, thank God. They can keep their leave. *I* don't want seven nights in an Anderson. I'd rather stay here, I would.'

Old Fred never stopped talking once he started. The soldier tapped the counter with a shilling and leaned over to see whether the barmaid was on the other side of the partition. He saw her silky legs and the flutter of her skirt. He hit the counter harder, then, while he waited, wondered at his impatience. His body wasn't thirsty; it was too damned tired to bother, too worn-out. It was something else in him that wanted to get drunk, dead, dead drunk.

The barmaid came along, smiling. She was natural with the soldiers. She smiled when she saw who it was and held her pretty clenched fist to him across the counter. He should have taken it and forced it gently open, of course. Instead, he just put his flat palm underneath it. She looked at him with a hurt-faun reproach in her sailing eyes, and opening her hand let a toffee fall into his.

'One from the wood, Madge,' he said.

'I'll have to charge you for *that*,' she said.

'That's all right,' he replied. 'You always pay in this life.'

'Why don't you take the girl, Taffy?' said old

Fred as he came and sat by them, their darts over.
'If I was your age –'

He had been in the army since he was fifteen.
Now he was past soldiering, wandering in the head
sometimes, doing odd jobs; in peace-time he kept
the lawns trimmed at the depot, now he was tin-
man in the cooking-shed, cleaning with Vim the
pots and pans Ben Bryant used for cooking.
'Vermicelli tastes all right,' he said. 'Better than
anything you can pick up in the streets. Yellow or
black or white, German or Irish. I've never had a
Russian though, never. It's not bad when you're
young, like a new crane when the jib runs out nice
and smooth; it's better than sitting in the trenches
like an old monkey, scratching yourself and not
knowing whose leg it is or whose arm it is, looking
in his pockets to see if there's anything worth
taking, and not knowing who'll win the race, the
bullet with your number on it or the leaky rod
you're nursing. But I like it here. It's nice and
peaceful up here, in the cookhouse all day. We
ought to try some vermicelli, Ben, one day.'

'Don't you get impatient now, Freddy,' Ben said
with the calmness of a father of many children.
'We'll stuff your pillow full of it next Christmas and
put a sprig of it on your chest. Don't you worry,
boy.'

But old Fed went on talking like an old prophet
in a volcanic world, about and about. 'There's no

knowing when you've got to fight for your king and country,' he said. 'No matter who you are, Russian or Frenchy or Jerry – and the Yankee, too. He'll be in it, boy. I've seen him die. It's only natural, to my way of thinking. I wore a pair of gloves the Queen knitted herself, she did, last time. The Unknown Soldier I was, last time.'

None of us are ourselves now, the Welsh boy sat thinking: neither what we were, nor what we will be. He drained his pint glass and crossed to the counter, to Madge smiling there.

'You never looked round all the way up from the station,' she said, pulling her shoulder-straps up under her grey jumper and exposing the white rich flesh above her breasts.

'So it was you followed me, eh?' he said, sardonic.

'Why didn't you turn round?' she asked. 'Did you know it was me? You knew someone was behind you, I could tell.'

'I didn't turn round because I didn't want to look *back*,' he said.

'And you mean to say you don't know how the Hebrew puts out the eyes of a goldfinch?' Freddy's aggrieved voice swirled up.

'Afraid of being homesick for your wife, eh?' she jeered.

He covered his eyes with his hand, tired out, and looked up at the vague sensual woman playing upon his instincts there like a gipsy on a zither.

'Not homesick,' he said drily. 'Death-sick.'

'What d'you mean?' she said.

'Well, she was killed in a raid,' he shouted.

He went up to the orderly room then, having forgotten to hand in his leave pass to the orderly corporal. The room was in the corner of an old warehouse. The building also housed the kitchen and the quartermaster's stores. About the high bare rooms with their rotten dry floors and musty walls rats galloped in the darkness; in the morning their dirt lay fresh on the mildewed sacks and the unit's cat stretched her white paws and got a weak and lazy thrill from sniffing it.

The orderly corporal was dozing over a Western novelette from Woolworth's, hunched up in a pool of lamp-and-fire-light.

'Hallo, Taffy,' he said. 'Had a good leave?'

'Yes thanks,' he replied. 'Except for raids. Am I on duty to-morrow?'

'You're on duty to-night, I'm afraid,' the orderly corporal replied with the unctuous mock-regret of one who enjoys detailing tired or refractory men for unexpected jobs. 'Dave Finley had a cold on his chest this morning and didn't get out of bed. So they fetched him out on a stretcher and the M.O. gave him pneumonia pills before Dave could stop him; so he's got pneumonia now. You'll go on guard duty at midnight and at six hours.'

'O.K.'

He turned to go.

'Better get some sleep,' said the orderly corporal, yawning noisily. 'Hell! I'm browned off with this war.'

The soldier yawned too, and laughed, and returned to the barrack room to lie down for a couple of hours. He rolled his blankets down on the floor and stretched out.

Old Ben and Fred were back, also, Ben fixing bachelor buttons into his best trousers and singing Nelly Dean comfortably to himself, Fred muttering by the stove. 'There's some mean and hungry lads in this room,' he said; 'very hungry and mean. It's an awful nature, that. They'll borrow off you all right, but they won't lend you the turd off their soles. And always swanking in the mirror, and talking all the time, saying Yes, they can do the job easy. The fools! Whip 'em! Whip 'em!'

Ben was toasting bread on the point of his bayonet and boiling water in his billy. A tin of pilchards left over from tea was for them all.

'Come on, Taffy. Have a bellyful while you can,' he said.

'No thanks,' said the soldier, restless on his blankets. 'I don't feel like food to-night, Ben, thanks.'

'Ain't you never bin hungry?' Fred shouted

angrily. 'You don't know what food is, you youngsters don't.'

'I've been without food,' the soldier said, thinking of the '26 strike; and going without peas and chips in the chip shop by the town clock in college when a new book must be bought. But not now, when everything is free but freedom, and the doctor and dentist and cobbler send you no bills.

What survives I don't know, the soldier thought, rubbing his hot eyelids and shifting his legs on the spread-out blankets. What is it that survives?

He got up and buckled his battle order together, adjusting his straps, slipping the pull-through through his Enfield, polishing boots and buttons, tightening his helmet strap under his chin.

'There was a religious woman used to come to our house,' Ben was saying, 'and one day she said to me, sociable like, "You're a Guinness drinker, aren't you, Mr Bryant?" and I says "I am, mum," and she says "Well, can you tell me what's wrong with the ostrich on them advertisements?" '

The soldier went out to relieve the guard.

They were only twenty soldiers altogether, sent up here to guard a transmitting station hidden in the slopes of the Downs. A cushy job, safe as houses. There was a little stone shed, once used for sheep that were sick after lambing, in a chalky hollow on the forehead of the hill, which the guard used for sleeping in when they were off duty. Two hours on, four hours off, rain and sun and snow and stars. As the soldier toiled up the lane and across the high meadow to the shed, the milky moon came out from grey clouds and touched with lucid fingers the chopped branches piled in precise lengths at the foot of the wood. The pine trees moved softly as the moon touched their grey-green leaves, giving them a veil that looked like rainy snow, grey-white.

The lane running up through the wood shortened alarmingly in perspective. A star fell. So surprising, so swift and delicate, the sudden short curved fall and extinction of the tiny lit world. But over it the Plough still stayed, like something imperishable in man. He leant against the gate, dizzy and light-headed, waves of soft heat running into his head. He swallowed something warm and thick; spitting it out, he saw it was blood. He stayed there a little, resting, and then went on.

He went along the sandy lane, noticing as he always did the antique sculptures of sea and ice and rain, the smooth twisted flints, yellow and blue and mottled, lying in the white sand down which the water of winter scooped its way.

At the top of the lane was the lambing shed – guard room. He slipped quickly through the door to prevent any light escaping. There was gun-fire and the sound of bombs along the coast.

The sergeant of the guard was lying on a palliasse in front of the stove. He got up slowly, groaning lazily. 'So you're back again, Taffy, are you?' he said, a grudge in his too hearty welcome. 'Relieving Dave Finley, eh? He's swinging the lead, Dave is. I've a good mind to report him to the O.C. It's tough on you, going on night guard after a day's journey. Have a good leave, Taff?'

'Not bad,' the soldier replied, 'except for the raids. Raided us the first night I was home.'

'It's a sod, everybody's getting it,' the sergeant replied, yawning. 'They dropped two dozen incendiaries in our fields in Lincs. last week.'

He was drinking a billy can of cocoa which he had boiled on the fire, but he didn't offer any. He had weak blue eyes, a receding chin, fresh features of characterless good-looks, wavy hair carefully combed and brilliantined. He was always on edge against Taffy, distrusting him, perhaps envying him. He lived in terror of losing a stripe and in constant hunger to gain another promotion. He sucked and scraped the officers for this, zealously carrying out their orders with the finnicky short temper of a weak house-proud woman. He polished the barrack room floor and blackleaded the stove himself because the boys refused to do more than give the place a regulation lick. And he leaped at the chance of putting a man on the peg, he was always waiting to catch somebody cutting a church parade or nipping out of camp to meet a girl when he should be on duty. Yet he was mortally afraid of a quarrel, of unpopularity, and he was always jovial, glassily jovial, even to the Welsh boy whom he knew he couldn't deceive.

'Who am I to relieve on guard?' the soldier asked.

'Nobby Sherraton. He's patrolling the ridge.'

'O.K.' He slipped his rifle sling over his shoulder and put his helmet on. 'You marching me out? Or shall I just go and see Nobby in?'

For once laziness overcame discretion.

'There's nobody about. Just go yourself,' the sergeant said, smiling, posing now as the informal honest soldier. 'I'll be seeing yer.'

'Some day.'

He left the hut and crossed the dry dead-white grass to the ridge where Nobby was on guard.

Nobby was his mate.

He had only been in the unit about a month. Before that he had been stationed just outside London and had done a lot of demolition and rescue work. He was from Mile End, and had roughed it. His hands and face showed that, his rough blackened hands, cigarette-stained, his red blotchy face with the bulbous nose, and the good blue eyes under tiny lids, and short scraggy lashes and brows. His hair was mousy and thin. He had been on the dole most of the time. He had been an unsuccessful boxer; he cleared out of that game when his brother, also a boxer, became punchdrunk and blind. He had plenty of tales of the Mosley faction. He was sometimes paid five bob to break up their meetings. He always took his five bob but he let the others do the breaking up. Who wants a black eye and a cut face for five bob? 'Tain't worth it. He rarely said anything about women. He didn't think much of lots of them; though like all Cockney youths he loved the 'old lady', his mother. He wasn't married. No, sir.

He was a conscript. Naturally. He didn't believe in volunteering. And he didn't like the Army, its drills and orders and its insistence on a smart appearance. Smartness he disliked. Appearances he distrusted. Orders he resented. He was 'wise' to things. No sucker.

Taffy felt a warm little feeling under his skin, relief more than anything else, to see Nobby again. He hadn't to pretend with Nobby. Fundamentally they shared the same humanity, the unspoken humanity of comradeship, of living together, sharing what they had, not afraid to borrow or talk or shut up. Or to leave each other and stroll off to satisfy the need for loneliness.

Nobby was surprised so much that he flung out his delight in a shout and a laugh and a wave of his arms. 'Taffy, lad!' he said. 'Back already, eh? Boy!' Then he became normal.

'Can't keep away from this bloody sannytorium for long, can we?' he grumbled.

Taffy stood looking at him, then at the ground, then he turned away and looked nowhere.

'What's wrong, kid?' Nobby said, his voice urgent and frightened, guessing. 'Anything bad? Caught a packet, did you?' He said the last two phrases slowly, his voice afraid to ask.

'*I* didn't,' Taffy said, his voice thin and unsteady. '*I* didn't. *I'm* all right. *I'm* healthy.'

Nobby put his hand on his shoulder and turned him round. He looked at the white sucked-in face and the eyes looking nowhere.

'Did *she* get it?' and he too turned his head a little and swallowed. 'She did,' he said, neither asking a question nor making a statement. Something absolute, the two words he said.

Taffy sat down, stretched out. The grass was dead; white, wispy long grass; Nobby sat down, too.

'They came over about eight o'clock the first night,' Taffy said. 'The town hadn't had a real one before. I've told you we've only got apartments, the top rooms in an old couple's house. The old ones got hysterics, see, Nobby. And then they wouldn't do what I told them, get down the road to a shelter. They wouldn't go out into the street and they wouldn't stay where they were. 'My chickens,' the old man was blubbering all the time.

He's got an allotment up on the voel, see? Gwyneth made them some tea. She was fine, she calmed them down. That was at the beginning, before the heavy stuff began. I went out the back to tackle the incendiaries. The boy next door was out there, too. He had a shovel and I fetched a saucepan. But it was freezing, and we couldn't dig the earth up quick enough. There were too many incendiaries. One fell on the roof and stuck in the troughing. The kid shinned up the pipe. It exploded in his face and he fell down. Twenty odd feet. I picked him up and both his eyes were out, see?'

He had gone back to the sing-song rhythm and the broad accent of his home, the back lanes and the back gardens. He was shuddering a little, and sick-white, sallow.

Nobby waited.

'I took him into his own house,' he said, controlling his voice now, almost reflective. 'I left him to his sister, poor kid. Then I went in to see if Gwyneth was all right. She was going to take the old couple down the road to the shelter. She had a mack on over her dressing gown. We'd intended going to bed early, see? So I said she was to stay in the shelter. But she wanted to come back. We could lie under the bed together.

'I wanted her back, too, somehow. Then some more incendiaries fell, so I said "Do as you like" and went at them with a saucepan. I thought sure one would blow my eyes out. Well, she took them down. Carried their cat for them. Soon as she'd gone the heavy stuff came. Oh Christ!'

Nobby let him go on; better let him go on.

'It knocked me flat, dazed me for a bit. Then I got up and another one flattened me. It was trying to stop me, see, Nobby. I crawled out of the garden, but it was dark as hell and buildings all down, dust and piles of masonry. Then he dropped some more incendiaries and the fires started. I knew she must be somewhere, see? I knew she must be somewhere. I began pulling the masonry away with my hands, climbed on to the pile of it in the fire. I couldn't see with the smoke and I knew it wasn't any use, only I had to do it, see?

'Then suddenly the masonry fell downwards. The road was clear on the other side. I thought it was all right after all, then. I thought she'd have reached the shelter . . . But she hadn't.

'I found her about twenty yards down the road.

'She wasn't dead. Her clothes were gone. And her hands. She put them over her face, I reckon.

'She couldn't speak, but I knew she knew it was me.

'I carried her back in my arms. Over the fallen house. The fire wasn't bad by then. Took her home, see, Nobby. Only the home was on fire. I wanted her to die all the time. I carried her over a mile through the streets. Fires and hoses and water. And she wouldn't die. When I got her to the clearing station I began to think she'd live.

'But they were only playing a game with me, see?'

He stood up and made himself calm.

'Well there it is.' He rubbed his face with the palm of his hand, wiping the cold sweat off.

'I knew she was going to die. When they told me she was – I didn't feel anything, Nobby.

'But she died while they were messing her body about with their hands, see?

'And she never said anything. Never said anything to me.

'Not that it makes any difference, I suppose. We never did speak about those things much. Only, you know how it is, you want a word somehow. You want it to keep.'

'Sure. I know,' Nobby said.

'What's it all for, Nobby?' he said in a while. He looked so tired and beat. 'I used to know what it was all about, but I can't understand it now.'

'Aw, forget all about that,' Nobby said. 'You're here, aincher, now?'

He put his hands on his mate's shoulders and let him lean against him for a bit.

'I reckon you belong to each other for keeps, now,' Nobby said.

'You believe that, Nobby?' he asked, slow and puzzled, but with a gathering force as his uncertainty came together.

'Yes. For you and 'er, I do. It wouldn't be true for me, or the sergeant in there, but for you two it is.'

Taffy was still against his shoulder. Then slowly he straightened himself, moved back onto himself, and lifting his face he looked at the milky-white fields and the sentinel pines and the stars.

'I knew it was so, really,' he said. 'Only I was afraid I was fooling myself.'

He smiled, and moved his feet, pressing on them with his whole weight as if testing them after an illness.

'I'm all right now, Nobby. Thank you, boy.'

'I'll go, then,' Nobby said. He slipped his rifle over his shoulder and as he moved off he hesitated, turned back, and touched his mate's arm lightly.

'Two's company, three's none,' he said, and stumped off slowly to the lambing shed through the dead straw-grass.

And the soldier was left alone on the flat upland ridge.

Below him the valleys widened into rich arable lakes on which the moonlight and the mist lay like the skeins which spiders spin round their eggs. Beyond the pools another chain of downland lay across the valleys, and beyond those hills the coast. Over him, over the valleys, over the pinewoods, blue fingers came out of the earth and moved slanting across their quarters as the bombers droned in the stars over his head and swung round to attack the coastal city from inland. The sky over the coast was inflamed and violent, a soft blood-red.

The soldier was thinking of the day he received his calling up papers, just a year ago. Sitting on the dry-stone wall of his father's back garden with Gwyneth by him; his ragged little brother kneeling by the chicken-run, stuffing cabbage stumps through the netting for the hens to peck, and laughing and pulling the stumps out as the old hen made an angry jab; his father riddling the ashes and the ramshackle garden falling to bits, broken trellis and tottering fence; his mother washing her husband's flannel vest and drovers in the tub, white and vexed. He had taken Gwyneth's hand, and her hand had said, 'In coming and in going you are mine; now, and for a little while longer; and then for ever.'

But it was not her footsteps that followed him down the lane from the station.

Now over his head the darkness was in full leaf, drifted with the purity of pines, the calm and infinite darkness of an English night, with the stars moving in slow declension down the sky. And the warm scent of resin about him and of birds and of all small creatures moving in the loose mould in the ferns like fingers in velvet.

And the soldier stood under the pines, watching the night move down the valleys and lift itself seawards, hearing the sheep cough and farm-dogs restlessly barking in the farms. And farther still the violence growing in the sky till the coast was a turbulent thunder of fire and sickening explosions, and there was no darkness there at all, no sleep.

'My life belongs to the world,' he said. 'I will do what I can.'

He moved along the spur and looked down at the snow-grey ever-green woods and the glinting roofs scattered over the rich land.

And down in the valleys the church bells began pealing, pealing, and he laughed like a lover, seeing his beloved.

The Orange Grove

The grey truck slowed down at the crossroads and the Army officer leaned out to read the signpost. *Indians Only*, the sign pointing to the native town read. *Dak Bungalow* straight on. 'Thank God,' said Staff-Captain Beale. 'Go ahead, driver.' They were lucky hitting a dak bungalow at dusk. They'd bivouacked the last two nights, and in the monsoon a bivouac is bad business. To-night they'd be able to strip and sleep dry under a roof, and heat up some bully on the Tommy cooker. Bloody good.

These bungalows are scattered all over India on the endless roads and travellers may sleep there, cook their food, and pass on. The rooms are bare and whitewashed, the verandah has room for a camp bed, they are quiet and remote, tended for the Government only by some old khansama or chowkey, usually a slippered and silent old Moslem. The driver pulled in and began unpacking the kit, the dry rations, the cooker, the camp bed, his blanket roll, the tin of kerosene. Beale went off to find the caretaker, whom he discovered squatting amongst the flies by the well. He was a wizened yellow-skinned old man in a soiled dhoti. Across his left breast was a plaster, loose and dripping with pus, a permanent discharge it seemed. He wheezed as he replied to the brusque request and raised himself with pain, searching slowly for his keys.

Beale came to give the driver a hand while the old man fumbled with the crockery indoors.

'The old crow is only sparking on one cylinder,' he said. 'Looks like T.B.,' he added with the faint overtone of disgust which the young and healthy feel for all incurable diseases. He looked out at the falling evening, the fulgurous inflammation among the grey anchorages of cloud, the hot creeping prescience of the monsoon.

'I don't like it to-night,' he said. 'It's eerie; I can't breathe or think. This journey's getting on my nerves. What day is it? I've lost count.'

'Thursday, sir,' the driver said, 'August 25.'

'How do you know all that?' Beale asked, curious.

'I have been thinking it out, for to write a letter to-night,' the driver said. 'Shall I get the cooker going, sir? Your bed is all ready now.'

'O.K.' Beale said, sitting on his camp bed and opening his grip. He took out a leather writing-pad in which he kept the notes he was making for Divisional H.Q., and all the letters he'd received from home. He began looking among the letters for one he wanted. The little dusty driver tinkered with the cooker. Sometimes Beale looked up and watched him, sometimes he looked away at the night.

This place seemed quiet enough. The old man

had warned him there was unrest and rioting in the town. The lines had been cut, the oil tanks unsuccessfully attacked, the court house burnt down, the police had made lathi charges, the district magistrate was afraid to leave his bungalow. The old man had relished the violence of others. Of course you couldn't expect the 11th to go by without some riots, some deaths. Even in this remote part of Central India where the native princes ruled from their crumbling Mogol forts through their garrisons of smiling crop-headed little Ghurkas. But it seemed quiet enough here, a mile out of the town. The only chance was that someone might have seen them at the cross roads; it was so sultry, so swollen and angry, the sky, the hour. He felt for his revolver.

He threw the driver a dry box of matches from his grip. Everything they carried was fungoid with damp, the driver had been striking match after match on his wet box with a curious depressive impassivity. Funny little chap, seemed to have no initiative, as if some part of his will were paralysed. Maybe it was that wife of his he'd talked about the night before last when they had the wood fire going in the hollow. Funny, Beale had been dazed with sleep, half listening, comprehending only the surface of the slow, clumsy words. Hate. Hate. Beale couldn't understand hate. War hadn't taught it to him, war was to him only fitness, discomfort, feats of endurance, proud muscles, a career, irresponsible dissipation, months of austerity broken by 'blinds' in Cairo, or Durban, Calcutta or Bangalore or Bombay. But this little rough-head with his soiled hands and bitten nails, his odd blue eyes looking away, his mean bearing, squatting on the floor with kerosene and grease over his denims – he had plenty of hate.

' . . . tried to emigrate first of all, didn't want to stay anywhere. I was fourteen, finished with reformatory schools for keeps . . . New Zealand I wanted to go. There was a school in Bristol for emigrants . . . I ran away from home but they didn't bother with me in Bristol, nacherly . . . Police sent me back. So then I became a boy in the Army, in the drums, and then I signed on. I'm a time-serving man, sir; better put another couple of branches on the fire; so I went to Palestine, against the Arabs; seen them collective farms the Jews got there, sir? Oranges . . . then I come home, so I goes on leave . . . We got a pub in our family and since my father died my mother been keeping it . . . for the colliers it is . . . never touch beer myself, my father boozed himself to death be'ind the counter. Well, my mother 'ad a barmaid, a flash dame she was, she was good for trade, fit for an answer any time, and showing a bit of her breasts every time she drew a pint. Red hair she had, well not exactly red, I don't know the word, not so *coarse* as red. My mother said for me to keep off her. My mother is a big Bible woman, though nacherly she couldn't go to chapel down our way being she kept a pub . . . Well, Monica, this barmaid, she slept in the attic, it's a big 'ouse, the Bute's Arms. And I was nineteen. You can't always answer for youself, can you? It was my pub by rights, *mine*. She was *my* barmaid. That's how my father'd have said if he wasn't dead. My mother wouldn't have no barmaids when he was alive. Monica knew what she was doing all right. She wanted the pub and the big double bed; she couldn't wait . . . It didn't seem much to pay for sleeping with a woman like that . . . Well, then I went back to barracks, and it wasn't till I told my mate and he called me a sucker that I knew I couldn't . . . Nothing went right after that. She took good care to get pregnant, Monica did, and my mother threw her out. But it was my baby, and I married her without telling my mother. It was *my* affair, wasn't it? *Mine*.'

How long he had been telling all this Beale couldn't remember. There was nothing to pin that evening upon; the fire and the logs drying beside the fire, the circle of crickets, the sudden blundering of moths into the warm zone of the fire and thoughtful faces, the myopic sleepy stare of fatigue, and those bitter distasteful words within intervals of thought and waiting. Not until now did Beale realize that there had been no hard-luck story told, no gambit for sympathy or compassionate leave or a poor person's divorce. But a man talking into a wood fire in the remote asylums of distance, and slowly explaining the twisted and evil curvature of his being.

'She told me she'd get her own back on me for my mother turning her out . . . And she did . . . I know a man in my own regiment that slept with her on leave. But the kid is mine. My mother got the kid for me. She shan't spoil the kid. Nobody'll spoil the kid, neither Monica nor me . . . I can't make it out, how is it a woman is so wonderful, I mean in a bedroom? I should 'a' murdered her, it would be better than this, this hating her all the time. Wouldn't it? . . . '

'The Tommy cooker's O.K. now, sir,' the driver said. 'The wind was blowing the flame back all the time. O.K. now with this screen. What's it to be? There's only bully left.'

'Eh? What?' Beale said. 'Oh, supper? Bully? I can't eat any more bully. Can't we get some eggs or something? Ten days with bully twice a day is plenty. Can you eat bully?'

'Can't say I fancy it,' the driver said. 'I'll go down the road and see if I can get some eggs.'

'I shouldn't bother,' Beale said. 'The storm will get you if you go far. Besides, it is dangerous down the town road. They've been rioting since Gandhi and Nehru were arrested last week. Better brew up and forget about the food.'

Beale was by nature and by his job as a staff officer one who is always doing things and forgetting about them. It was convenient as well as necessary to him. His *Pending* basket was always empty. He never had a load on his mind.

'I'll take a walk just the same,' the driver said. 'Maybe I'll find a chicken laying on the road. I won't be long.'

He was a good scrounger, it was a matter of pride with him to get anything that was wanted, mosquito poles, or water or anything. And every night, whether they were in the forest or the desert plains that encompass Indore, he had announced his intention of walking down the road.

Some impulse caused Beale to delay him a moment.

'Remember,' Beale said, 'the other night, you said you saw the collective farms in Palestine?'

'Aye,' said the driver, standing in the huge deformity of the hunch-backed shadow that the lamp projected from his slovenly head.

'They were good places, those farms?' Beale asked.

'Aye, they were,' the driver said, steadying his childish gaze. 'They didn't have money, they didn't buy and sell. They shared what they had and the doctor and the schoolteacher the same as the labourer or the children, all the same, all living together. Orange groves they lived in, and I would like to go back there.'

He stepped down from the porch and the enormous shadows vanished from the roof and from the wall. Beale sat on, the biscuit tin of water warming slowly on the cooker, the flying ants casting their wings upon the glass of the lamp and the sheets of his bed. An orange grove in Palestine . . . He was experiencing one of those enlargements of the imagination that come once or perhaps twice to a man, and recreate him subtly and profoundly. And he was thinking simply this – that some things are possible and other things are impossible to us. Beyond the mass of vivid and sensuous impressions which he had allowed the war to impose upon him were the quiet categories of the possible and the quieter frozen infinities of the impossible. And he must get back to those certainties . . . The night falls, and the dance bands turn on the heat. The indolent arrive in their taxis, the popsies and the good-timers, the lonely good-looking boys and the indifferent erotic women. Swing music sways across the bay from the urbane permissive ballrooms of the Taj and Green's. *In the Mood, It's foolish but it's fun*, some doughboys cracking whips in the coffee-room, among apprehensive glances, the taxi drivers buy a betel leaf and spit red saliva over the running-board, and panders touch the sleeves of the soldiers, the crowd huddles beneath the Gateway, turning up collars and umbrellas everywhere against the thin sane arrows of the rain. And who is she whose song is the world spinning, whose lambent streams cast their curved ways about you and about, whose languors are the infinite desires of the unknowing? Is she the girl behind the grille, in the side street where they play gramophone records and you pay ten chips for a whisky and you suddenly feel a godalmighty yen for whoever it is in your arms? But beyond that? Why had he failed with this woman, why had it been impossible with that woman? He collected the swirl of thought and knew that he could not generalize as the driver had done in the glow of the wood fire. Woman. The gardener at the boarding school he went to used to say things about women. Turvey his name was. Turvey, the headmaster called him, but the boys had to say *Mr* Turvey. Mr Turvey didn't hold with mixed bathing, not at any price, because woman wasn't clean like man, he said. And when the boys demurred, thinking of soft pledges and film stars and the moon, Mr Turvey would wrinkle his saturnine face and say, 'Course you young gentlemen knows better than me. I only been married fifteen years. I don't know nothing of course.' And maybe this conversation would be while he was emptying the ordure from the latrines into the oil drum on iron wheels which he trundled each morning down to his sewer pits in the school gardens.

But in an intenser lucidity Beale knew he must not generalize. There would be perhaps one woman out of many, one life out of many, two things possible – if life itself were possible, and if he had not debased himself among the impossibilities by then. The orange grove in Palestine . . .

And then he realized that the water in the biscuit tin was boiling and he knelt to put the tea and tinned milk into the two enamel mugs. As he knelt a drop of rain the size of a coin pitted his back. And another. And a third. He shuddered. Ten days they'd been on the road, making this reconnaissance for a projected Army exercise, and each day had been nothing but speed and distance hollow in the head, the mileometer ticking up the daily two hundred, the dust of a hundred villages justifying their weariness with its ashes, and to-morrow also only speed and distance and the steadiness of the six cylinders. And he'd been dreaming of a Bombay whore whose red kiss he still had not washed from his arm, allowing her to enter where she would and push into oblivion the few things that were possible to him in the war and the peace. And now the rain made him shudder and he felt all the loneliness of India about him and he knew he had never been more alone. So he was content to watch the storm gather, operating against him from a heavy fulcrum in the east, lashing the bungalow and the trees, infuriating the night. The cooker spluttered and went out. He made no move to use the boiling water upon the tea. The moths flew in from the rain, and the grasshoppers and the bees. The frogs grunted and croaked in the swirling mud and grass, the night was animate and violent. He waited without moving until the violence of the storm was spent. Then he looked at his watch. It was, as he thought. The driver had been gone an hour and twenty minutes. He knew he must go and look for him.

He loaded his revolver carefully and buckled on his holster over his bush shirt. He called for the old caretaker, but there was no reply. The bungalow was empty. He turned down the wick of the lamp and putting on his cap, stepped softly into the night. It was easy to get lost. It would be difficult to find anything to-night, unless it was plumb in the main road.

His feet felt under the streaming water for the stones of the road. The banyan tree he remembered, it was just beyond the pull-in. Its mass was over him now, he could feel it over his head. It was going to be difficult. The nearest cantonment was four hundred miles away; in any case the roads were too flooded now for him to retrace his way to Mhow. If he went on to Baroda, Ahmedabad – but the Mahi river would be in spate also. The lines down everywhere, too. They would have to go on, that he felt sure about. Before daybreak, too. It wasn't safe here. If only he could find the driver. He was irritated with the driver, irritated in a huge cloudy way, for bungling yet one more thing, for leaving him alone with so much on his hands, for insisting on looking for eggs. He'd known something would happen.

He felt the driver with his foot and knelt down over him in the swirling road and felt for his heart under his sodden shirt and cursed him in irritation and concern. Dead as a duckboard, knifed. The rain came on again and he tried to lift up the corpse the way he'd been taught, turning it first on to its back and standing firmly astride it. But the driver was obstinate and heavy and for a long time he refused to be lifted up.

He carried the deadweight back up the road, sweating and bitched by the awkward corpse, stumbling and trying in vain to straighten himself. What a bloody mess, he kept saying; I told him not to go and get eggs; did he have to have eggs for supper? It became a struggle between himself and the corpse, who was trying to slide down off his back and stay lying on the road. He had half a mind to let it have its way.

He got back eventually and backed himself against the verandah like a lorry, letting the body slide off his back; the head fell crack against the side wall and he said 'Sorry,' and put a sack between the cheek and the ground. The kid was soaking wet and wet red mud in his hair; he wiped his face up with cotton-waste and put a blanket over him while he packed the kit up and stowed it in the truck. He noticed the tea and sugar in the mugs and tried the temper of the water. It was too cold. He regretted it. He had the truck packed by the end of half an hour, his own bedding roll stretched on top of the baggage ready for the passenger. He hoped he'd be agreeable this time. He resisted a bit but he had stiffened a little and was more manageable. He backed him into the truck and then climbed in, pulling him on to the blankets by his armpits. Not until he'd put up the tailboard and got him all ready did he feel any ease. He sighed. They were away. He got into the driving seat to switch on the ignition. Then he realized there was no key. He felt a momentary panic. But surely the driver had it. He slipped out and, in the darkness and the drive of the rain, searched in the man's pockets. Paybook, matches, identity discs (must remember that, didn't even know his name), at last the keys.

He started the engine and let her warm up, slipped her into second, and drove slowly out. The old caretaker never appeared, and Beale wondered whether he should say anything of his suspicions regarding the old man when he made his report. Unfortunately there was no evidence. Still, they were away from there; he sighed with relief as the compulsion under which he had been acting relaxed. He had this extra sense, of which he was proud, of being able to feel the imminence of danger as others feel a change in the weather; it didn't help him in Libya, perhaps it hindered him there; but in a pub in Durban it had got him out in the nick of time; he'd edged for the door before a shot was fired. He knew to-night all right. The moment he saw that dull red lever of storm raised over his head, and the old caretaker had shrugged his shoulders after his warning had been laughed off. You had to bluff them; only sometimes bluff wasn't enough and then you had to get away, face or no face. Now he tried to remember the route on the map; driving blind, the best thing was to go slow and pull in somewhere a few miles on. Maybe the sun would rise sometime and he could dry out the map and work out the best route; no more native towns for him; he wanted to get to a cantonment if possible. Otherwise he'd look for the police lines at Dohad or Jabhua or wherever the next place was. But every time he thought of pulling in, a disinclination to stop the engine made him keep his drenched ammunition boot on the accelerator pedal. When he came to a road junction he followed his fancy; there is such a thing as letting the car do the guiding.

He drove for six hours before the night stirred at all. Then his red-veined eyes felt the slight lessening in the effectiveness of the headlights that presaged the day. When he could see the red berm of the road and the flooded paddy-fields lapping the bank, he at last pulled up under a tree and composed himself over the wheel, placing his cheek against the rim, avoiding the horn at the centre. He fell at once into a stiff rigid sleep.

A tribe of straggling gipsies passed him soon after dawn. They made no sound, leading their mules and camels along the soft berm on the other side of the road, mixing their own ways with no other's. The sun lay back of the blue rain-clouds, making the earth steam. The toads hopped out of the mud and rested under the stationary truck. Land-crabs came out of the earth and sat on the edge of their holes. Otherwise no one passed. The earth seemed content to let him have his sleep out. He woke about noon, touched by the sun as it passed.

He felt guilty. Guilty of neglect of duty, having slept at his post? Then he got a grip on himself and rationalized the dreadful guilt away. What could he have done about it? The driver had been murdered. What did they expect him to do? Stay there and give them a second treat? Stay there and investigate? Or get on and report it. Why hadn't he reported it earlier? How could he? The lines were down, the roads flooded behind him, he was trying his best; he couldn't help sleeping for a couple of hours. Yet the guilt complex persisted. It was a bad dream and he had some evil in him, a soft lump of evil in his brain. But why? If he'd told the man to go for eggs it would be different. He was bound to be all right as long as he had his facts right. Was there an accident report form to be filled in immediately, in duplicate, Army Form B – something-or-other? He took out his notebook, but the paper was too wet to take his hard pencil. 23.00 hrs. on 23 August 1942 deceased stated his desire to get some eggs. I warned him that disturbances of a political character had occurred in the area . . . He shook himself, bleary and sore-throated, in his musty overalls, and thought a shave and some food would put him right. He went round to the back of the truck. The body had slipped with the jolting of the road. He climbed in and looked at the ashen face. The eyes were closed, the face had sunk into an expressionless inanition, it made him feel indifferent to the whole thing. Poor sod. Where was his hate now? Was he grieving that the woman, Mona was it, would get a pension out of him now? Did he still hate her? He seemed to have let the whole matter drop. Death was something without hate in it. But he didn't want to do anything himself except shave and eat and get the whole thing buttoned up. He tore himself away from the closed soiled face and ferreted about for his shaving kit. He found it at last, and after shaving in the muddy rain-water he ate a few hard biscuits and stuffed a few more into his pocket. Then he lashed the canvas down over the tailboard and got back to the wheel. The truck was slow to start. The bonnet had been leaking and the plugs were wet in the cylinder heads. She wouldn't spark for a minute or two. Anxiety swept over him. He cursed the truck viciously. Then she sparked on a couple of cylinders, stuttered for a minute as the others dried out, and settled down steadily. He ran her away carefully and again relaxed. He was dead scared of being stranded with the body. There wasn't even a shovel on the truck.

After driving for an hour he realized he didn't know where he was. He was in the centre of a vast plain of paddy-fields, lined by raised bunds and hedged with cactus along the road. White herons and tall fantastic cranes stood by the pools in the hollows. He pulled up to try and work out his position. But his map was nowhere to be found. He must have left it at the dak bungalow in his haste. He looked at his watch; it had stopped. Something caved inside him, a sensation of panic, of an enemy against whose machinations he had failed to take the most elementary precautions. He was lost.

He moved on again at once. There was distance.

The mileometer still measured something? By sunset he would do so many miles. How much of the day was left? Without the sun how could he tell? He was pannicky at not knowing these things; he scarcely knew more than the man in the back of the truck. So he drove on and on, passing nobody but a tribe of gipsies with their mules and camels, and dark peasants driving their bullocks knee-deep in the alluvial mud before their simple wooden ploughs. He drove as fast as the track would allow; in some places it was flooded and narrow, descending to narrow causeways swept by brown streams which he only just managed to cross. He drove till the land was green with evening, and in the crepuscular uncertainty he halted and decided to kip down for the night. He would need petrol; it was kept in tins in the back of the truck; it meant pulling the body out, or making him sit away in a corner. He didn't want to disturb the kid. He'd been jolted all day; and now this indignity. He did all he had to do with a humility that was alien to him. Respect he knew; but this was more than respect; obedience and necessity he knew, but this was more than either of these. It was somehow an admission of the integrity of the man, a new interest in what he was and what he had left behind. He got some soap and a towel, after filling his tanks, and when he had washed himself he propped the driver up against the tailboard and sponged him clean and put P.T. shoes on his feet instead of the boots that had so swollen his feet. When he had laid him out on the blankets and covered him with a sheet, he rested from his exertions, and as he recovered his breath he glanced covertly at him, satisfied that he had done something for him. What would the woman have done, Monica? Would she have flirted with him? Most women did, and he didn't discourage them. But this woman, my God, he'd bloody well beat her up. It was her doing, this miserable end, this mess-up. He hadn't gone down the road to get eggs; he'd gone to get away from her. It must have been a habit of his, at nights, to compose himself. She'd bitched it all. He could just see her. And she still didn't know a thing about him, not the first thing. Yes, he hated her all right, the voluptuous bitch.

He slept at the wheel again, falling asleep with a biscuit still half chewed in his mouth. He had erotic dreams, this woman Monica drawing him a pint, and her mouth and her breasts and the shallow taunting eyes; and the lights in her attic bedroom with the door ajar, and the wooden stairs creaking. And the dawn then laid its grey fingers upon him and he woke with the same feeling of guilt and shame, a grovelling debased mood, that had seized him the first morning. He got up, stretching himself, heady with vertigo and phlegm, and washed himself in the paddy flood. He went round to the back of the truck to get some biscuits. He got them quietly, the boy was still sleeping, and he said to himself that he would get him through to-day, honest he would. He had to.

The sun came out and the sky showed a young summer blue. The trees wakened and shook soft showers of rain off their leaves. Hills showed blue as lavender and when he came to the cross-roads he steered north-west by the sun, reckoning to make the coast road somewhere near Baroda. There would be a cantonment not far from there, and a Service dump for coffins, and someone to whom he could make a report. It would be an immense relief. His spirits rose. Driving was tricky; the worn treads of the tyres tended to skid, the road wound up and down the ghats, through tall loose scrub, but he did not miss seeing the shy jungle wanderers moving through the bush with their bows, tall lithe men like fauns with black hair over their eyes that were like grapes. They would stand a moment under a tree, and glide away back into the bush. There were villages now, and women of light olive skin beating their saris on the stones, rhythmically, and their breasts uncovered.

And then, just when he felt he was out of the lost zones, in the late afternoon, he came down a long sandy track through cactus to a deep and wide river at which the road ended. A gipsy tribe was fording it and he watched them to gauge the depth of the river. The little mules, demure as mice, kicked up against the current, nostrils too near the water to neigh; the camels followed the halter, stately as bishops, picking their calm way. The babies sat on their parents' heads, the women unwound their saris and put them in a bundle on their crowns, the water touched their breasts. And Beale pushed his truck into bottom gear and nosed her cautiously into the stream. Midway across the brown tide swept up to his sparking plugs and the engine stopped. He knew at once that he was done for. The river came up in waves over the sideboards and his whole concern was that the boy inside would be getting wet. A gipsy waded past impersonally, leading two bright-eyed grey mules. Beale hailed him. He nodded and went on. Beale called out 'Help!' The gipsies gathered on the far bank and discussed it. He waved and eventually three of them came wading out to him. He knew he must abandon the truck till a recovery section could be sent out to salvage it, but he must take his companion with him, naturally. When the gipsies reached him he pointed to the back of the truck, unlaced the tarpaulin and showed them the corpse. They nodded their heads gravely. Their faces were serious and hard. He contrived to show them what he wanted and when he climbed in they helped him intelligently to hoist the body out. They contrived to get it on to their heads, ducking down under the tailboard till their faces were submerged in the scum of the flood.

They carried him ashore that way, Beale following with his revolver and webbing. They held a conclave on the sand while the women wrung out their saris and the children crowded round the body. Beale stood in the centre of these lean outlandish men, not understanding a word. They talked excitedly, abruptly, looking at him and at the corpse. He fished his wallet out of his pocket and showed them a five-rupee note. He pointed to the track and to the mules. They nodded and came to some domestic agreement. One of them led a little mule down to the stream and they strapped a board across its bony moulting back, covering the board with sacking. Four of them lifted the body up and lashed it along the spar. Then they smiled at Beale, obviously asking for his approval of their skill. He nodded back and said 'That's fine.' The gipsies laid their panniers on the mules, the women wound their saris about their swarthy bodies, called their children, formed behind their men. The muleteer grinned and nodded his head to Beale. The caravanserai went forward across the sands. Beale turned back once to look at the truck, but he was too bloody tired and fed up to mind. It would stay there; it was settled in; if the floods rose it would disappear; if they fell so much the better. He couldn't help making a balls of it all. He had the body, that was one proof; they could find the truck if they came to look for it, that was the second proof. If they wanted an accident report they could wait. If they thought he was puddled they could sack him when they liked. What was it all about, anyway?

Stumbling up the track in the half-light among the ragged garish gipsies he gradually lost the stiff self-consciousness with which he had first approached them. He was thinking of a page near the beginning of a history book he had studied in the Sixth at school in 1939. About the barbarian migrations in pre-history; the Celts and Iberians, Goths and Vandals and Huns. Once Life had been nothing worth recording beyond the movements of people like these, camels and asses piled with the poor property of their days, panniers, rags, rope, gramm and dahl, lambs and kids too new to walk, barefooted, long-haired people rank with sweat, animals shivering with ticks, old women striving to keep up with the rest of the family. He kept away from the labouring old women, preferring the tall girls who walked under the primitive smooth heads of the camels. He kept his eye on the corpse, but he seemed comfortable enough. Except he was beginning to corrupt. There was a faint whiff of badness about him . . . What did the gipsies do? They would burn him, perhaps, if the journey took too long. How many days to Baroda? The muleteer nodded his head and grinned.

Well, as long as he had the man's identity discs and paybook, he would be covered. He must have those . . . He slipped the identity discs over the wet blue head and matted hair and put them in his overall pocket. He would be all right now, even if they burned him . . . It would be a bigger fire than the one they had sat by and fed with twigs and talked about women together that night, how many nights ago?

He wished, though, that he knew where they were going. They only smiled and nodded when he asked. Maybe they weren't going anywhere much, except perhaps to some pasture, to some well.

For further reading

Poems

Raiders' Dawn and other poems (George Allen and Unwin, 1942)

Ha! Ha! Among the Trumpets (George Allen & Unwin, 1943)

Selected Poetry and Prose, ed. Ian Hamilton (George Allen & Unwin, 1966)

Selected Poems, ed. Jeremy Hooker and Gweno Lewis (Unwin Paperbacks, 1981)

Collected Poems, ed. Cary Archard (Seren, 1994)

Prose

The Last Inspection (George Allen & Unwin, 1943)

In the Green Tree (George Allen & Unwin, 1948)

Alun Lewis: a miscellany of his writings, ed. John Pikoulis (Poetry Wales Press, 1982)

Letters to my Wife, ed. Gweno Lewis (Seren, 1989)

Collected Stories, ed. Cary Archard (Seren, 1994)

Biography and criticism

Alun John, *Alun Lewis* in the *Writers of Wales* series (University of Wales Press, 1970)

John Pikoulis, *Alun Lewis, a Life* (Seren, 1984: new edn. 1991)

Images of Wales

The Corgi Series covers, no.6
Alun Lewis wood engraving, 1941, by John Petts, used as a frontispiece for Alun Lewis' first book of poems, Raiders' Dawn

John Petts (1914-1991) was one of the outstanding wood-engravers of the twentieth century. His stunning prints featuring Welsh mountains and the people who live amongst them reflect his deep concern for the history of the land and are distinguished by the profound understanding of the physical and psychological properties of light.

In 1935, John Petts and Brenda Chamberlain abandoned their studentship at the Royal Academy Schools, London, for a rundown farmhouse in the rugged terrain of Snowdonia. They started the Caseg Press in 1937 in the hope that it might finance their freedom to work. At first dedicated to saleable ephemera such as Christmas cards and bookplates, the press later became involved in the broader Welsh cultural scene, providing illustrations for the *Welsh Review*, a monthly literary periodical. In 1941, with the writer Alun Lewis, the Caseg Press produced a series of broadsheets designed to express continuity and identification with the life of rural Wales in the face of social change precipitated by the second world war.

From *John Petts and the Caseg Press* by Alison Smith.

For all enquiries please contact:

MARTIN TINNEY GALLERY
www.artwales.com
18 St Andrew's Crescent
Cardiff CF10 3DD
tel: 029 20641411
mtg@artwales.com